CHÂTEAU-MYSTÈRE
MYSTERY CASTLE

Illustrated by Brenda Haw

Adapted from Puzzle Castle, in the Usborne Young Puzzles series, by
Kathy Gemmell

Bilingual editor: Nicole Irving
Design adaptation by John Russell

Language consultant: Lorraine Sharp

Original story by Susannah Leigh
Edited by Gaby Waters
Designed by Paul Greenleaf

Contents

About this book

This book is about a brave knight called Sophie and her adventure at Mystery Castle. The story is in French and English. You can look up the word list on page 23 if you want to check what any French word means. This list also shows you how to say each French word.

Sophie

Château-Mystère

There is a puzzle on every double page. Solve each one and help Sophie on her way. All the French words you need to solve the puzzles are in the word keys (look out for this sign: 🗝). If you get stuck, the answers are on page 22.

L'histoire The story

L'ami de Sophie, Simon, habite le Château-Mystère. Il lui a écrit cette lettre:

Sophie's friend, Simon, lives in Mystery Castle. He has written her this letter:

Simon

Château-Mystère	Mystery Castle
Chère Sophie,	Dear Sophie,
Tu es invitée, ce soir, au banquet du château.	You are invited to the castle banquet this evening.
Il commencera à six heures.	It will start at six.
Nous avons un petit problème.	We have a little problem.
Il y a un monstre quelque part dans les oubliettes.	There is a monster somewhere in the dungeons.
Tu es très, très, très courageuse.	You are very, very, very brave.
Peux-tu venir en avance pour trouver le monstre?	Can you come early and find the monster?
Ton ami, Simon	Your friend, Simon

Things to look for

When Sophie gets to the castle, she must collect the seven things shown here. They will all help her to find the monster. You will find one of them on each double page, from the moment she sees the castle, until she reaches the dungeons.

le parapluie vert
green umbrella

la lampe de poche extra-puissante
extra-powerful flashlight

les chaussures-vitesse
run-fast shoes

le bouclier anti-monstre
anti-monster shield

le dictionnaire du langage monstre
monster-language dictionary

le casque anti-monstre
anti-monster helmet

la clé
key

Thomas, the ghost

Mystery Castle is haunted by a friendly ghost, called Thomas. He is hiding on every double page. See if you can spot him.

Jim, the juggler

Jim is working on his juggling for the banquet, but he is not very good at it. He has lost his juggling balls around the castle. There is at least one hiding on every double page. Can you find them?

The juggling balls look like this.

How to sound French

Here are a few tips to help you say French sounds and letters in a French way.

The letter à is said like the "a" in "cat", â like the "a" in "part", ai, è, and ê like the "e" in "sell", é like the "a" in "late" and i like the "i" in "machine". You often say the French e and eu like the "u" in "fur". To say u, round your lips as if to say "oo", then try to say "ee". Say au and eau like the "o" in "rose" and oi like the "wa" in "wagon".

You never say h and you do not usually say s, t or r at the end of a word; n is often said like the "n" in "aunt", ch sounds like the "sh" in "show" and j sounds like the "s" in "measure". The French r is rolled at the back of your mouth, a little like gargling.

Le château The castle

Sophie se met tout de suite en route pour le château.
Sophie sets off for the castle at once.

Elle dit au revoir à ses parents.
She says goodbye to her parents.

Elle arrive bientôt aux douves du château.
Soon she arrives at the castle moat.

Mais quel chemin doit-elle prendre pour traverser?
But which route must she take to cross?

Le lapin lui donne la première indication.
The rabbit gives her the first direction.

**Can you spot the rabbit?
Follow all the directions and find the right
way to cross the moat.**

4

Key

tourne	turn
va	go
à droite	right
à gauche	left
tout droit	straight ahead
prends	take
ne prends pas	do not take
le pont	the bridge
ce pont	this bridge
vert	green
bleu	blue
passage interdit	no entry
au secours	help
bienvenue	welcome
au revoir	goodbye

Le plan The map

Sophie trouve Simon devant le hall du château. Il lui donne un plan du château.

Sophie finds Simon outside the castle entrance hall. He gives her a map of the castle.

"Le monstre est dans les oubliettes. Pour y arriver, tu dois aller à la cave."

"The monster is in the dungeons. To get there, you have to go to the cellar."

"En chemin, tu dois rendre visite à quatre personnes."

"On the way, you must visit four people."

"Tout le monde se prépare pour le banquet. Chaque personne a besoin de ton aide."

"Everybody is getting ready for the banquet. Each person needs your help."

Can you match the four people on the list with the rooms where Sophie will find them? She must visit them in order. Which route will she take to the cellar?

Sophie doit trouver:
Sophie must find:

1. Justin, le gardien des portraits
Justin, the portrait keeper

2. La princesse Fleur
Princess Fleur

3. Eric, le guetteur
Eric, the look-out boy

4. Madame Croûton, la cuisinière
Mrs. Croûton, the cook

Key 🔑

la tour de guet	look-out tower
le grenier	attic
le bureau	study
la chambre de…	…'s bedroom
la galerie des portraits	portrait gallery
le hall	entrance hall
les oubliettes	dungeons
la grande salle	banquet hall
la cuisine	kitchen
la salle de bain	bathroom
l'escalier	stairs
la cave	cellar
le garage	garage
la bibliothèque	library

Plan du château Map of the castle

la tour de guet

le grenier

le bureau

la chambre de Simon

la chambre de Fleur

la bibliothèque

la grande salle

la galerie des portraits

la salle de bain

le hall

la cuisine

l'escalier

le garage

la cave

les oubliettes

7

La galerie des portraits
The portrait gallery

Sophie visite d'abord la galerie des portraits.
Sophie's first visit is to the portrait gallery.

Justin, le gardien des portraits, est inquiet.
Justin, the portrait keeper, is worried.

"Oncle Stan vient au banquet."
"Uncle Stan is coming to the banquet."

"Je dois le rencontrer près des douves, mais j'ai oublié comment il est."
"I have to meet him by the moat, but I've forgotten what he looks like."

Which portrait is Uncle Stan's? There is only one which fits what everyone is saying.

8

La chasse au trésor
The treasure hunt

Ensuite, Sophie rend visite à la princesse Fleur.
Next, Sophie visits Princess Fleur.

Elle est dans sa chambre. Quel désordre!
She is in her bedroom. What a mess!

"Te voilà, Sophie!" crie Fleur.
"There you are, Sophie!" shouts Fleur.

"J'ai perdu mon collier, mon bracelet, ma bague et
ma couronne."
"I've lost my necklace, my bracelet, my ring and my crown."

Plusieurs autres choses ont disparu.
Several other things have disappeared.

**Can you find a necklace, bracelet, ring and crown
that match? Read the speech bubbles and point
to all the other things that have gone missing.**

La tour de guet The look-out tower

Sophie quitte la princesse. Elle monte à la tour de guet.
Des gens arrivent déjà pour le banquet.
Sophie leaves the princess. She climbs up to the look-out tower.
People are already arriving for the banquet.

Eric, le guetteur, ne sait pas si tout le monde est invité.
"Sophie," crie-t-il, "fais quelque chose!"
Eric, the look-out boy, does not know if everyone is invited.
"Sophie," he cries, "do something!"

Using Eric's list, can you help Sophie tell him which of the people in the picture are not invited? What treatment will they get?

La liste d'Eric

La reine de Jonville, Juliette: invitée.
La reine de Montfort, Marianne: pas invitée - traitement au fumier.
La princesse de Gouache, Géraldine: invitée.
La reine de Gaumont, Géraldine: pas invitée - traitement à la soupe à l'oignon.
La reine de Beaufort, Béatrice: pas invitée - traitement à la confiture.
Le roi de Roquefort, Roland: invité.
Le prince de Roquefort, Boris, et son chien, Fang: pas invités - traitement aux oeufs pourris.

OEUFS POURRIS

FUMIER

CONFITURE

SOUPE À L'OIGNON

Key

je m'appelle	my name is	(le) traitement au/à la/aux	treatment
je viens de	I come from		
la liste	list	(les) oeufs pourris	rotten eggs
le roi	king	(le) fumier	dung
la reine	queen	(la) soupe à l'oignon	onion soup
le prince	prince	(la) confiture	jam
la princesse	princess	son chien	his dog
invité(e)	invited	de/d'/des	of
pas invité(e)(s)	not invited	et	and

Dans la cuisine In the kitchen

Ensuite, Sophie va à la cuisine.
Next, Sophie goes to the kitchen.

Madame Croûton a l'air inquiet.
Mrs. Croûton looks worried.

"Qu'est-ce qu'il y a?" demande Sophie.
"What's the matter?" asks Sophie.

"Je dois faire un grand gâteau pour le banquet, mais je ne trouve pas tous les ingrédients."
"I must bake a big cake for the banquet, but I can't find all the ingredients."

"Je sais qu'ils sont ici quelque part."
"I know they're here somewhere".

Can you spot all the ingredients Mrs. Croûton is looking for somewhere in the kitchen?

14

Key 🔦

je cherche	I am looking for
un	one OR a
deux	two
trois	three
quatre	four
un pot de	a pot of
(le) miel	honey
(les) oeufs	eggs
(les) pains	loaves of bread
(le) citron	lemon
(les) prunes rouges	red plums
(le) sucre	sugar
(la) farine	flour
(le) fromage	cheese
(le) lait	milk
(l') eau	water
frais	fresh
et	and

La cave The cellar

Sophie quitte la cuisine et descend dans la cave.
Sophie leaves the kitchen and goes down to the cellar.

"Oh," dit-elle, en regardant le plan, "il y a beaucoup de portes ici."
"Oh," she says, looking at the map, "there are lots of doors here."

"Quelle est la bonne porte pour aller aux oubliettes?"
"Which is the right door to get to the dungeons?"

Heureusement pour Sophie, les animaux qui habitent la cave disent toujours la vérité.
Luckily for Sophie, the animals who live in the cellar always tell the truth.

Can you work out from what all the animals are saying which door Sophie should take?

16

Dans les oubliettes In the dungeons

Enfin, Sophie entre dans les oubliettes.
At last, Sophie enters the dungeons.

Elle entend des voix bizarres.
She hears strange voices.

"Simon m'a prévenue," dit-elle.
"Simon warned me about this," she says.

"Les animaux qui habitent ici ne disent jamais la vérité."
"The animals who live here never tell the truth."

"Je dois toujours faire le contraire de ce qu'ils disent."
"I must always do the opposite of what they say."

Read what the animals are saying. Can you give Sophie the correct directions to find the monster?

Did you remember to look for all Sophie's useful equipment? Look back to page 3 to check you have found everything.

Key

ouvre	open
n'ouvre pas	do not open
la porte	the door
tourne	turn
ne tourne pas	do not turn
à droite	right
à gauche	left
comment tu t'appelles?	what is your name?
je m'appelle	my name is
j'ai perdu	I have lost
ma maman	my mummy
la clé	the key

Tourne à droite.

Tourne à gauche

Sophie met ses chaussures-vitesse,...
Sophie puts on her run-fast shoes,...

...son casque et son bouclier.
...her helmet and her shield.

Tourne à droite.

Le banquet The banquet

C'est l'heure du banquet.
It is time for the banquet.

Sophie et le petit monstre s'amusent bien. Les vois-tu?
Sophie and the little monster are having a great time.
Can you see them?

Tout le monde est très content, mais plusieurs invités
ont perdu des choses.
Everyone is very happy, but several guests
have lost things.

Sophie ne peut pas tous les aider.
Sophie cannot help them all.

**Can you spot all the things that people are
looking for? Who will be especially pleased
to see the little monster?**

20

Key 🔑

French	English
où est	where is
le chat	the cat
la souris	the mouse
le cochon	the pig
le pain	the bread
la porte	the door
mon, ma	my
(le) nounours	teddy bear
(la) soupe	soup
(le) fils	son
verte	green

Answers

Pages 4-5

The route Sophie should take is shown in red.

Pages 6-7

Sophie's route will take her to: Justin in la galerie des portraits (the portrait gallery), Fleur in la chambre de Fleur (Fleur's bedroom), Eric in la tour de guet (the look-out tower) and Mrs. Croûton in la cuisine (the kitchen).

Pages 8-9

This is Uncle Stan's portrait.

Pages 10-11

Fleur's matching jewels are circled in red. All the other missing objects are circled in blue.

Pages 12-13

Boris, le prince de Roquefort and his dog, Fang are not invited. They will get the rotten egg treatment.

Pages 14-15

The missing ingredients are circled in red.

Pages 16-17

Sophie should go through this door.

Pages 18-19

Here are the correct directions: Tourne à gauche. Tourne à droite. Tourne à gauche. Tourne la clé. Ouvre la porte.

The monster is crying because he has lost his mum.

Pages 20-21

All the things that people are looking for are circled in red. Sniff's mum is especially pleased to see him. Here she is.

Did you spot everything?

Pages	Juggling balls	Equipment to find
4-5	one	anti-monster shield
6-7	one	key
8-9	three	extra-powerful flashlight
10-11	four	run-fast shoes
12-13	two	green umbrella
14-15	four	monster-language dictionary
16-17	two	anti-monster helmet
18-19	one	none here!
20-21	nineteen	none here!

Did you remember to look out for Thomas the ghost? Look back and find him on every double page.

Word list and pronunciation guide

Here is a list of all the French words and phrases used in this book. All the naming words (nouns) have le, la, l' or les before them. These all mean "the". In French, all nouns are either masculine or feminine. You use le with masculine nouns and la with feminine nouns; l' or les nouns have [m] or [f] after them to show if they are masculine or feminine. When you see les, it means the noun is plural (more than one).

Some French describing words (adjectives) change when they describe feminine nouns. Here, the masculine version is written first, followed by the feminine word. When an adjective describes a plural noun, it usually has an "s" on the end, for example: les prunes rouge_s_ (red plums).

Each French word in this list has its pronunciation shown after it (*in letters like this*). Read these pronunciation letters as if they were English words. You will sometimes see (n) or (m), which you should say slightly through your nose, as if you had a cold. You can read more about how to say French words on page 3.

French	Pronunciation	Meaning
à	*ah*	to
...a besoin	*ah buhzwa(n)*	...needs
à droite	*ah drwat*	(to the) right
à gauche	*ah gawsh*	(to the) left
l'aide [f]	*led*	help
aider	*edday*	to help
...a l'air	*ah lair*	...seems OR looks
aller	*alay*	to go
l'ami [m]	*lamee*	friend
les animaux [m]	*laiz aneemo*	animals
arriver	*areevay*	to arrive
au, à la, à l', aux	*oh, ah la, ah l, oh*	to the OR at the
au revoir	*oh ruh vwar*	goodbye
au secours	*oh suhkoor*	help
aussi	*ohsee*	also
autre	*ohtr*	other
avec	*avek*	with
la bague	*la bag*	ring
le banquet	*luh bo(n)kay*	banquet
la barbe	*la barb*	beard
beaucoup	*bokoo*	a lot
la bibliothèque	*la beebly otek*	library
bientôt	*bee a(n)toh*	soon
bienvenue	*bee a(n)vuhnew*	welcome
bizarre	*beezar*	strange
bleu, bleue	*bluh*	blue
bon, bonne	*bo(n), bonn*	good
bonjour	*bo(n)joor*	hello
le bouclier	*luh booklee ay*	shield
le bracelet	*luh brasslay*	bracelet
le bureau	*luh bewro*	study
le casque	*luh kask*	helmet
la cave	*la kav*	cellar
ce, cette	*suh, set*	this
c'est	*sai*	it is
la chambre	*la sho(m)br*	bedroom
chaque	*shak*	each
la chasse au trésor	*la shass oh traizor*	treasure hunt
le chat	*luh sha*	cat
le château	*luh shatoh*	castle
les chaussures [f]	*lay show sewr*	shoes
le chemin	*luh shuhma(n)*	way OR path
cher, chère	*sher, shair*	dear
le cheval	*luh shuhval*	horse
les cheveux [m]	*lay shuhvuh*	hair
le chien	*luh shee a(n)*	dog
les choses [f]	*lay shoz*	things
cinq	*sa(n)k*	five
le citron	*luh seetro(n)*	lemon
la clé	*la klay*	key
le cochon	*luh kosho(n)*	pig
le collier	*luh kollee ay*	necklace
comment il est	*kommo(n) eel ai*	what he looks like
comment tu t'appelles?	*kommo(n) tew tapell*	what is your name?
la confiture	*la ko(n)feetewr*	jam
content, contente	*ko(n)to(n), ko(n)to(n)t*	happy
le contraire	*luh ko(n)trair*	opposite
le cor	*luh kor*	horn
courageux, courageuse	*koorashuh koorashuhz*	brave
la couronne	*la kooronn*	crown
...crie	*kree*	...shouts
le croûton	*luh krooto(n)*	crouton
la cuisine	*la kweezeen*	kitchen
la cuisinière	*la kweezeen yair*	cook
d'abord	*dabor*	first
dans	*do(n)*	in
de	*duh*	of
déjà	*daysha*	already
...demande	*duhmo(n)d*	...asks
...descend	*desso(n)*	...goes down
deux	*duh*	two
devant	*duhvo(n)*	in front of
le dictionnaire	*luh deeks yonair*	dictionary
dit-elle	*deet el*	she says
doit-elle	*dwat el*	must she
...donne	*don*	...gives
les douves [f]	*lay doov*	moat
du, de la, de l', des	*dew, duh la, duh l, day*	of the
l'eau [f]	*loh*	water
elle	*el*	she, it

23

elle arrive	*el areev*	she arrives
elle dit	*el dee*	she says
elle doit	*el dwa*	she must
elle entend	*el o(n)to(n)*	she hears
elle monte	*el mo(n)t*	she climbs
elle regarde	*el ruhgard*	she looks (at)
en	*o(n)*	in
en avance	*o(n) avo(n)ss*	early
en chemin	*o(n) shuhma(n)*	on the way
en regardant	*o(n) ruhgardo(n)*	looking (at)
les enfants [m]	*laiz o(n)fo(n)*	children
enfin	*o(n)fa(n)*	at last
ensuite	*o(n)sweet*	next, then
...entre (dans)	*o(n)tr (do(n))*	...enters
l'escalier [m]	*lesskal yay*	stairs
...est	*ai*	...is
et	*ay*	and
faire	*fair*	to do OR to make
fais	*fai*	do
la farine [f]	*la fareen*	flour
le fils	*luh feess*	son
les fleurs [f]'	*lay flur*	flowers
la flûte (à bec)	*la flewt (ah bek)*	recorder
frais, fraîche	*frai, fraish*	fresh
le fromage	*luh fromajsh*	cheese
le fumier	*luh fewm yay*	dung
la galerie des portraits	*la galree day portrai*	portrait gallery
le garage	*luh garajsh*	garage
le gardien	*luh gardee a(n)*	keeper
le gâteau	*luh gatoh*	cake
les gens [m/f]	*lay sho(n)*	people
gentil, gentille	*sho(n)tee, sho(n)teey*	nice
grand, grande	*gro(n), gro(n)d*	big
la grande salle	*la gro(n)d sal*	banquet hall
le grenier	*luh gruhnee ay*	attic
le guetteur	*luh gettuhr*	look-out boy
...habite	*abeet*	...lives in
le hall	*luh al*	entrance hall
l'heure [f]	*luhr*	time
...heures [f]	*uhr*	...o'clock
heureusement	*uhruhzmo(n)*	luckily
l'histoire [f]	*leesstwar*	story
ici	*eessee*	here
il	*eel*	he, it
il a	*eel a*	he has
il a écrit	*eel a aikree*	he has written
il commencera	*eel kommo(n)suhra*	it will start
il est	*eel ai*	he is
il n'a pas de/d'	*eel na pa duh/d*	he does not have a (OR any)
il porte	*eel port*	he has OR he wears OR he carries
ils arrivent	*eelzareev*	they arrive
ils disent	*eel deez*	they say
il s'habille	*eel sabeey*	he dresses
ils sont	*eel so(n)*	they are
il y a	*eel ee a*	there is OR there are
l'indication [f]	*la(n)deekassee o(n)*	direction
les ingrédients [m]	*laiz a(n)graidee o(n)*	ingredients
inquiet, inquiète	*a(n)kee ai, a(n)k yet*	worried
invité, invitée	*a(n)veetai*	invited
les invités [m]	*laiz a(n)veetai*	guests
j'ai oublié	*shai ooblee yai*	I have forgotten
j'ai perdu	*shai perdew*	I have lost
jamais	*shamai*	never
jaune	*shone*	yellow
je	*shuh*	I
je cherche	*shuh shersh*	I am looking for
je dois	*shuh dwa*	I must
je m'appelle	*shuh mapell*	my name is OR I am called
je ne trouve pas	*shuh nuh troov pa*	I cannot find
je sais	*shuh sai*	I know
je viens de	*shuh vee a(n) duh*	I come from
le lait	*luh lai*	milk
la lampe de poche	*la lo(m)p de posh*	flashlight
le langage	*luh lo(n)gajsh*	language
le lapin	*luh lapa(n)*	rabbit
le, la, l', les	*luh, la, l, lay*	the
la lettre	*la letr*	letter
la liste	*la leest*	list
lui	*lwee*	to him OR to her
les lunettes [f]	*lay lewnett*	glasses
mais	*mai*	but
la maman	*la mamo(n)*	mummy OR mum
...m'a prévenu(e)	*ma praivuhnew*	...warned me
...met	*mai*	...puts on
le miel	*luh meeyell*	honey
mon, ma, mes	*mo(n), ma, may*	my
le monstre	*luh mo(n)str*	monster
la montre	*la mo(n)tr*	watch
la moustache	*la mooss tash*	moustache
le mystère	*luh meess tair*	mystery
...ne peut pas	*nuh puh pas*	...cannot
ne prends pas	*nuh pro(n) pa*	do not take
...ne sait pas	*nuh sai pa*	...does not know
ne tourne pas	*nuh toorn pa*	do not turn
noir, noire	*nwar*	black
le nounours	*luh noonoorss*	teddy bear
nous avons	*noozavo(n)*	we have
n'ouvre pas	*noovruh pa*	don't open
le numéro	*luh newmairo*	number
les oeufs [m]	*laiz uh*	eggs
l'oignon [m]	*lonn yo(n)*	onion
l'oncle [m]	*lo(n)kl*	uncle

...ont disparu	o(n) deesparew	...have disappeared	le roi	luh rwa	king
...ont perdu	o(n) perdew	...have lost	rouge	roojsh	red
orange	oro(n)sh	orange			
les oubliettes [f]	laiz ooblee ett	dungeons	la salle de bain	la sal duh ba(n)	bathroom
où est..?	oo ai	where is..?	...s'amusent bien	sa mewz bee a(n)	...are having a great time
ouvre (la porte)	oovr (la port)	open (the door)			
			...se met en route	suh met o(n) root	...sets off
le pain	luh pa	bread	...se prépare	suh praipar	...is getting ready
les pains [m]	lay pa	loaves of bread	si	see	if
le parapluie	luh para plwee	umbrella	six	seess	six
les parents [m]	lay paro(n)	parents	le soir	luh swar	evening
pas invité,	paza(n)veetai	not invited	son, sa, ses	so(n), sa, say	his OR her
pas invitée			la soupe	la soop	soup
passage interdit	passajsh a(n)terdee	no entry	la souris	la sooree	mouse
la personne	la personn	person	le sucre	luh sewkr	sugar
petit, petite	puhtee, puhteet	little			
peux-tu..?	puh tew	can you..?	te voilà	tuh vwala	there you are
le plan	luh plo(n)	map	ton, ta, tes	to(n), ta, tay	your
plusieurs	plewz yuhr	several	toujours	tooshoor	always
le pont	luh po(n)	bridge	la tour de guet	la toor duh gai	look-out tower
la porte	la port	door	tourne	toorn	turn
le pot	luh po	pot	tous	tooss	all
pour	poor	for OR in order to	tout de suite	too duh sweet	at once
pourri, pourrie	pooree	rotten	tout droit	too drwa	straight ahead
premier, première	prem yai, prem yair	first	tout le monde	too luh mo(n)d	everyone
prendre	pro(n)dr	to take	le traitement	luh tretmo(n)	treatment
prends	pro(n)	take	traverser	traversay	to cross
près	prai	near	très	trai	very
le prince	luh pra(n)ss	prince	trois	trwa	three
la princesse	la pra(n)sess	princess	...trouve	troov	...finds
le problème	luh problaim	problem	trouver	troovay	to find
les prunes [f]	lay prewn	plums	tu dois	tew dwa	you must
puissant	pweesso(n),	powerful	tu es	tew ai	you are
puissante	pweesso(n)t				
			un, une	a(n), ewn	one OR a
quatre	katr	four			
que, qu'	kuh, k	that	va	va	go
quelle	kel	which OR what	venir	vuhneer	to come
quel désordre	kel daizordr	what a mess	la vérité	la vaireetai	truth
quelque chose	kelkuh shoz	something	vert, verte	vair, vairt	green
quelque part	kelkuh par	somewhere	...vient	vee a(n)	...comes
qu'est-ce qu'il y a?	kess keel ee a	what is the matter?	violet, violette	vee olay, vee olet	purple
...quitte	keet	...leaves	...visite	veezeet	...visits (a place)
			la vitesse	la veetess	speed
la reine	la ren	queen	vois-tu..?	vwa tew	can you see..?
rencontrer	ro(n)ko(n)tray	to meet	la voix	la vwa	voice
rendre visite à	ro(n)dr veezeet ah	to visit (a person)			
...rend visite à	ro(n) veezeet ah	...visits	y	ee	there

This bilingual edition first published in 1994 by Usborne Publishing Ltd., Usborne House, 83-85 Saffron Hill, London EC1N 8RT. Based on a previous title first published in 1992.

Copyright © 1994, 1992 Usborne Publishing Ltd.

Printed in Portugal